May the Creator
Bless You!
Glenna Loving

# Shenandoah, Daughter of the Stars

## A Children's Book

## Written and Illustrated
## by
## Glenna Loving

Cork Hill Press
Carmel

CORK HILL PRESS™

Cork Hill Press
597 Industrial Drive, Suite 110
Carmel, Indiana 46032-4207
1-866-688-BOOK
www.corkhillpress.com

Hardcover Edition: 1-59408-483-1

Library of Congress Card Catalog Number: 2004101010

**Printed in the United States of America**

**1 3 5 7 9 10 8 6 4 2**

The Shenandoah Valley lies between the Blue Ridge and the Allegheny Mountains. The Massanutten Mountain Range divides the valley for some forty miles. The name Massanutten meant "Potato Ground". The native people gathered roots of a starchy plant that grew on the mountain range.

The Shenandoah Valley, into which the first people came over 10,000 years B.C., takes its name from the river. The Shenandoah flows into two large branches, the North and the South Forks. The river makes seven bends like a silver ribbon as it flows northeast to the Potomac River. The river's name in the native language was Senedos or Sherando, which meant, "The Clear Eyed Daughter of the Stars".

The native people left little in the Shenandoah Valley except mounds to be plowed down, their tools, the dust of their bodies, and their bones. They were long gone when the first white men entered the valley. At this time the valley was the hunting grounds for the Delawares, Susquehanna, and the Catawbas of South Carolina. The native people did leave the river and the valley with their name, "Shenandoah".

Among traditional Native American cultures a name reflects one's identity. Names could derive from a closely connected circumstance, event, relative, or place. In some native cultures, names could be changed by the people after a life changing event or a vision. If the name change was after a spiritual event it reflected a change in identity.

Glenna Loving

For My Grandchildren Hunter, Haley, Loran, and Lenzi.
To the people who love and care for the Shenandoah River and Valley.

## Shenandoah
## "Daughter of the Stars"

Long ago the Creator formed a beautiful valley with a mountain range that extended through the valley like a "sleeping mother." The Creator also created a river of beauty and clear water to wind around the mountains on the valley floor. The native people called the river "Shenandoah" and to the mountain range they gave the name "Massanutten."

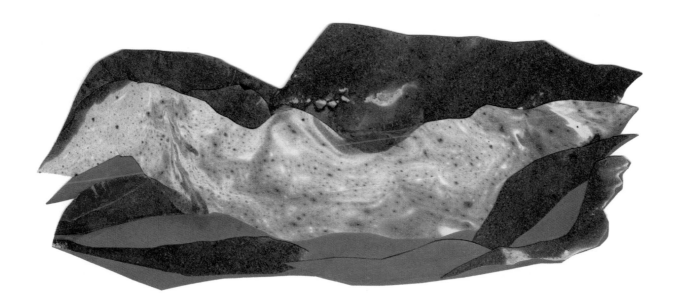

On a night when the Creator filled the blue, black sky with millions of stars that sparkled on the river, a baby's voice could be heard. The voice was strong and clear on the night wind. A girl child was born in the time of many flowers.

The grandmother handed the child to the father. She spoke, "The Creator has given you a child during the time of many flowers. She will be called "Little Flower". The father smiled as he whispered "Little Flower".

The Creator planted many trees and seeds on the mountains, in the valley and along the banks of the river.

Little Flower loved to go with the grandmothers to gather fruit, nuts, and flowers. The Grandmothers and other women would dry the flowers and plants for medicines and dyes, as well as for food. They would often weave the natural colors of the flowers into their baskets and other handwork.

The fruits and nuts made tasty meals. Some would be added to other foods. They would also be dried and used when the winter season came. In the winter the Creator gave rest to the plants and some animals. They would sleep until the time of many flowers.

Little Flower grew strong and beautiful. The people loved her gentle ways. They would say, "The Creator has made Little Flower beautiful in both body and spirit."

Sixteen seasons of many flowers had passed. On her sixteenth birth night, Little Flower stood on the bank of the clear sparkling river. She raised her arms to give thanks to the Creator and sang a song her mother had taught her.

Oh great Creator,
Your Gifts are wonderful.
You give your people
gifts of beauty.
Food from our mother
the earth.
Life from our brother
the river.
Your lodge is among
the stars.
I give you thanks for all
these gifts.

The mother and father watched their daughter as she sang her song of praise. As they watched and listened, something wonderful began to occur.

In a vision from the Creator, Little Flower walked to the edge of the river. She stepped on the surface of the sparkling water. Her deer skin robe changed to the colors of the sky after a summer storm. The colors were the Creator's promise to always care for his people. Little Flower lifted her hand to the night sky. The moon rested on her hand. Little Flower placed the moon back into its space among the stars as the Creator had intended.

The mother whispered "Our daughter is no longer Little Flower." The father agreed. "The creator wishes to give her a new name. Tomorrow we will prepare the ceremony for the giving of a new name."

On the evening of the "New Naming Ceremony", the people gathered. Little Flower's father spoke to the people. He told of the vision the Creator had shown to the mother and father. He said, "The Creator wishes the people to give Little Flower a new name."

The people all agreed, Little Flower would be given a new name. They said, "Her ways are gentle. She shares with the people the gifts from the Creator that she gathers from the valley and the Massanutten. Little Flower's beauty is like the clear sparkling river. The grandmothers will choose for her the new name."

The grandmothers spoke as one. "It was a vision by the Creator that Little Flower became the 'Clear Eyed Daughter of the Stars'. The new name has been chosen."

The people said, "She will no longer be called 'Little Flower'. Her new name will be 'Shenandoah'. She is the Daughter of the Stars."

## About the Author:

Glenna McBride Loving was born in Paradise, Texas. In 1957, she married her husband, Ray, in Fort Worth. They moved to Ray's home of Strasburg, Virginia, with their two young sons in 1960. Glenna worked for the Shenandoah County school system for thirty-two years. She has a love for Native-American Cultures and children's literature. The acrylic watercolor collage illustrations reflect her southwestern background.